Department of Education and S<

CW00393483

Mathematics from 5 to 16

Curriculum Matters 3
AN HMI SERIES

LONDON · HER MAJESTY'S STATIONERY OFFICE

First published 1985
ISBN 0 11 270577 4

Preface

This is the third in HM Inspectorate's discussion series *Curriculum Matters*. It sets out a framework within which each school might develop a mathematics programme appropriate to its own pupils.

The document focusses on the aims and objectives for the teaching of mathematics between the ages of 5 and 16 and considers their implications for the choice of content, for teaching approaches, and for the assessment of pupils' progress.

Like all other papers in this series, *Mathematics from 5 to 16* is a discussion document and the Inspectorate would welcome your comments and suggestions on it and the issues it raises. We would be particularly interested in comments and views about differentiation of objectives in relation to age and ability.

If you have any comments, please send them to the Staff Inspector (Mathematics), Department of Education and Science, York Road, London SE1 7PH, by 31 July 1985.

E J BOLTON
Senior Chief Inspector

Contents

Page

Introduction 1

1 The aims of mathematics teaching 2

2 Objectives 7

3 Criteria for content 26

4 Classroom approaches 35

5 Assessment 44

6 Implementation 52

Appendix 1 Mathematical objectives for most pupils at the ages of 11 and 16 54

Appendix 2 Differentiation: an illustrative example 62

Appendix 3 References 65

It is essential that this document should be read as a whole, since all sections are interrelated. For example, the lists of objectives must be seen in relation to the defined aims and to what is said about the principles of mathematics teaching and assessment.

Introduction

Mathematics has been the subject of considerable public debate for a number of years. Central to that debate has been the work of the Committee of Inquiry into the Teaching of Mathematics in Schools under the Chairmanship of Dr W H (now Sir Wilfred) Cockcroft. Since the publication in January 1982 of the report of that committee, *Mathematics counts*, the debate has involved a much wider public and has been more fully informed.

The purpose of the present paper is to focus attention on the **aims** and **objectives** for the teaching of mathematics from 5 to 16 and to consider their implications for the choice of **content**, the **approaches** to be used in the classroom and the **assessment** of pupils' performance. These five aspects are considered in Chapters 1 to 5 in turn, but they are interrelated and so the document needs to be read as a whole. This approach is similar to that suggested in previous publications such as *Mathematics 5 to 11* and *Curriculum 11 to 16: Towards a Statement of Entitlement*.

The ideas presented in the paper have considerable implications for the mathematics curriculum of all pupils throughout the age range 5 to 16 and across the whole ability range. Each school needs to develop its own strategy for any changes which may be necessary although in the final chapter some suggestions are made about a possible way of implementing the recommendations made. These will also have considerable implications for public examinations at 16-plus and for in-service training provision for teachers.

The paper draws on the evidence of inspection which suggests that there is a need for the regular review and evaluation of the mathematics in the school curriculum. Its aims, objectives, criteria for content, classroom approaches and assessment procedures cannot be determined for all time but must be subject to continuous development.

Comments and suggestions from individual readers of this document and from interested associations and institutions will be welcomed. They should be sent by 31 July 1985 to: the Staff Inspector (Mathematics), Department of Education and Science, Elizabeth House, York Road, London SE1 7PH.

1. The aims of mathematics teaching

1.1 There are important aims which should be an essential part of any general statement of intent for the teaching of mathematics. Those stated in this chapter are considered to be indispensable but it is recognised that there may be others which teachers will wish to add. These aims are intended for all pupils although the way they are implemented will vary according to their ages and abilities.

Mathematics as an essential element of communication

1.2 Mathematics can be used to describe, to illustrate, to interpret, to predict and to explain. Above all it is used to convey meaning. If pupils cannot interpret the result of a mathematical task then it has had little value for them: if they can perform successfully a multiplication involving two numbers but are unable to say, if challenged, when that operation might be used, or to say whether the answer is a reasonable one or not, then there is something seriously wrong. The main reason for teaching mathematics is its importance in the analysis and communication of information and ideas. The mere manipulation of numerical or algebraic symbols is of secondary importance.

Mathematics as a powerful tool

1.3 A tool enables things to be done which it might otherwise be impossible or difficult to do, or to do as well. Mathematics is such a tool. Many instances arise in the school curriculum, in working life and in society generally where mathematics is used as a tool in a variety of ways. Viewed from this perspective it is not the mathematics itself but the result obtained which is the important thing. The result might be a design in art, a model in craft, an analysis of an experiment in science, the checking of a shopping bill, the planning of a holiday, or the construction of a motorway and it is in that outcome that the interest lies. Skills such as measuring length, telling the time, constructing a graph, drawing geometric shapes, dividing one number by another and solving an equation are not important ends in themselves and only become so as they are embedded in purposeful activities. It is unfortunate that much of the work pupils do in mathematics should appear to them and to adults to lack purpose, as one submission to the Cockcroft Committee indicated:

"Mathematics lessons in secondary schools are very often not about anything. You collect like terms, or learn the laws of indices, with no perception of why anyone needs to do such things. There is excessive preoccupation with a sequence of skills and quite inadequate opportunity to see the skills emerging from the solution of problems." (*Mathematics counts*, para 462).

The aim is to encourage the effective use of mathematics as a tool in a wide range of activities within both school and adult life.

Appreciation of relationships within mathematics

1.4   Mathematics is not an arbitrary collection of disconnected items, but has a coherent structure in which the various parts are inter-related. In very simple terms *mathematics is about relationships*. For example, there are relationships between any two numbers which may be expressed in different forms: 18 may be said to be greater than 6, or 12 more than 6, or three times 6. Fractions, decimals and percentages are related. Properties of shapes may be related to patterns in number and algebra: for example, work on square numbers may be developed by building with unit squares; $(a+b)^2 = a^2 + 2ab + b^2$ can be approached geometrically by considering areas. And yet there is a danger in school mathematics that this fundamental feature of mathematics might not be appreciated by pupils as they become preoccupied with trying to master the details. At whatever level pupils are working the aim should be to enable them to appreciate that there are relationships between the different aspects of mathematics structure. There is no doubt that this would facilitate pupils' progress.

Awareness of the fascination of mathematics

1.5   There is a fascination about mathematics itself, irrespective of its utilitarian value, which it is possible to develop to some degree in most if not all pupils. This fascination will not,

3

of course, be the same for all pupils but most aspects, if considered within a suitable context and at an appropriate level, can have such an appeal. The spark may come from the feeling for order, the appreciation of pattern, an interesting relationship, the power of a formula, the simplicity of a generalisation, a curious or unexpected result, the conciseness of an abstraction, the aesthetic appeal of mathematical designs or models in two or three dimensions, or the elegance of a proof. Much will depend on the enthusiasm of the teachers and on the classroom approaches used.

Imagination, initiative and flexibility of mind in mathematics

1.6 When presented with a mathematical task pupils should be encouraged to find their own method of carrying it out even though there may be a standard, more streamlined method which they might ultimately learn. For example, pupils who can multiply by a single digit number might be challenged to find how to multiply by larger numbers. Such activities are a useful mathematical experience and, indeed, there is considerable evidence to indicate that many 'imposed methods', on which much time is spent in schools, are often quickly forgotten and that pupils or adults revert to their own methods which they understand and in which they are more confident. In this context there is a particular confusion over what is meant by the 'solution of problems' in mathematics. Many textbooks present 'problems' which use words and give the exact amount of information required for solution. These questions require pupils to make direct use of a skill which has just been learnt, but they provide relatively little real challenge. Opportunities need to be given to pupils to use their expertise to find their own ways through problems and investigations in which the strategies are not immediately obvious and where they need to show initiative and flexibility in their approach. The aim should be to show *mathematics as a process, as a creative activity* in which pupils can be fully involved, and not as an imposed body of knowledge immune to any change or development. Some topics from the history of mathematics, such as the development of the number system, can be illuminating for many pupils in this respect.

Working in a systematic way

1.7 Attention is usually given to careful and accurate execution of routine tasks such as number operations and the solution of equations, but a systematic approach in mathematics involves much more than that. It involves elements of appraisal and review as the execution of the task proceeds. Pupils need to think clearly, reflect on what an activity entails and consider what strategies are possible. In some cases the best strategy may be to use a standard method. In others the best strategy may be to approach the task in a free, exploratory way especially if it is problem solving which requires an investigative approach. But even this approach becomes systematic as the information obtained is analysed. Careful consideration also needs to be given to the 'final' result: this might involve checking the working, making a rough approximation to see whether the result is reasonable, giving any interpretation which may be necessary and, perhaps, extending the result in various ways. The aim that pupils should learn to work in a systematic way does not clash with the aim that they should learn to show imagination, initiative and flexibility of mind; the two aims are complementary.

Working independently

1.8   Success in teaching can be gauged, to some extent, by the way in which pupils have learnt to work effectively in an independent way. Such independence might be expressed in a variety of ways: pupils do not stop working and wait for the teacher to provide a lead when something slightly unfamiliar appears; they do not always rely on standard methods; if materials have to be used they obtain these without fuss; they learn when it is appropriate to use or not to use equipment such as tape measures, ready reckoners and calculators; they are able to do work based on 'real' material such as advertisements, printed forms and wage slips; they are able to work on a project using topic and reference books. There is a danger that mathematics might be made to appear to pupils to consist mainly of answering set questions, often of a trivial nature, to which the answers are already known and printed in the answer book! But *pupils will have developed well mathematically when they are asking and answering their own questions . . . why? . . . how? . . . what does that mean? . . . is there a better way? . . . what would happen if I changed that?. . . does the order matter?. . .*

Working cooperatively

1.9   In many primary schools pupils work in groups, but this

5

generally means that the pupils, although grouped, are actually working individually even if on similar tasks. 'Working cooperatively' is much more than that. It means working together on a common task where all the pupils in the group make a contribution. For example, a group of pupils might devise, carry out, analyse and write up a statistical survey. A group presentation to the rest of the class of the findings of the survey can also be productive. Investigational work and problem solving are often better done in small groups of two or three pupils. Similary some of the best work using microcomputers involves cooperation between two pupils and, indeed, one machine per pupil in a classroom is not usually the best arrangement for mathematical purposes. Cooperative activities contribute to the mathematical development of the pupils through the thinking, discussion and mutual refinement of ideas which normally take place. This aim emphasises the *interactive nature of mathematics*; it should be less of a solitary experience than it is at present.

In-depth study in mathematics

1.10   Much of the mathematical experience of most pupils is extremely fragmented, as they proceed from one small item to another in quick succession. Indeed, because of the commonly held view that 'many pupils cannot concentrate for any length of time' many textbooks are planned to provide this rapidly changing experience. However, provided that topics which interest them are selected it is possible to encourage most if not all pupils to pursue a study in some depth. Such work may be stimulated through a variety of means: the enthusiasm of the teacher; team teaching with lead lessons; interests of individual pupils or groups of pupils; the need for a survey of people's opinions; a range of attractive resource material; investigative activities; micro software; TV material; games; puzzles; hobbies. An in-depth study is of potential value for all pupils, not only mathematically but also in terms of the development of personal qualities such as commitment and persistence.

Pupils' confidence in their mathematical abilities

1.11   Mathematics should provide both a challenge and a sense of achievement for all pupils. That is, all pupils should be extended but no pupils should be so extended that they largely experience failure. To achieve this requires professional judgement in setting tasks which are differentiated according to the pupils involved. At present many teachers feel that they are under pressure from parents, from schools to which their pupils will transfer, from employers, and from examination requirements, to push pupils to cover mathematical content for which they are not ready. The mathematics syllabus should be reduced for the majority of pupils and re-designed in order that they may cover it thoroughly with useful activities at each stage. This would enable pupils to gain in confidence and come to be able to tackle mathematical tasks without anxiety and apprehension. Mathematics must be an experience from which pupils derive pleasure and enjoyment.

2. Objectives

2.1   In this chapter the aims of mathematics are followed through into more specific objectives. They are considered in five main categories:

A. FACTS
B. SKILLS
C. CONCEPTUAL STRUCTURES
D. GENERAL STRATEGIES
E. PERSONAL QUALITIES

Objectives C, D and E are more general than objectives A and B with the result that they often present more difficulty in terms both of classroom approaches and methods of assessment. Whatever difficulties there may be, each type of objective is an essential part of mathematics for all pupils and so needs to be given serious consideration.

2.2   It is the intention of this chapter to provide an overall framework of objectives. It is for teachers and schools to complete the details within this framework, paying attention especially to the considerable differentiation which will be needed under each heading for particular pupils or groups of pupils. An illustration of mathematical objectives at ages 11 and 16 is given in Appendix 1.

2.3   Placing objectives in categories helps to highlight the different elements in mathematical activities. There is, nevertheless, a danger in doing this, namely the development of classroom approaches which place the different objectives in watertight compartments and deal with them accordingly. The outcomes which it is hoped will accrue from this analysis are that teachers' awareness will be increased and that, within most if not all mathematical activities, each type of objective will be present to some degree although the emphasis will vary between different activities.

A. FACTS
(Objectives 1–4)

2.4 Pupils need to know and remember some basic mathematical facts at each level if progress is to be made with confidence, but the memory demands in mathematics can be much reduced through a sound conceptual understanding of the structure of the subject. Many pupils who are 'good at mathematics' have a relatively poor memory for factual details, but have a firm grasp of the principles. Nevertheless there are some things which need to be remembered.

Objective 1
Remembering terms

2.5 Pupils need to be introduced to mathematical terms such as names (numbers, shapes, operations . . .) and qualities (greater than, regular, odd and even, symmetrical . . .) and then over a period of time through frequent use to assimilate them. In comparison with many other subjects there are relatively few technical terms in mathematics but difficulties often arise because much of this vocabulary is used so infrequently that it does not become an integral part of mathematical language and activity. In particular, pupils are done a disservice if specialised vocabularly is avoided, for example, if 'the top line of a fraction' is always used instead of 'numerator' and 'a four-sided figure' is constantly used instead of 'quadrilateral'. Care needs to be taken that the initial use of a term is such that it does not

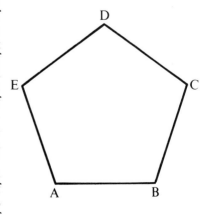

Figure 1

limit the pupils' understanding and create difficulties at a later stage. For example, a pupil who learns to associate the word 'pentagon' only with those pentagons which are regular (equal sides, equal interior angles) and have their bases horizontal (Figure 1) may have difficulty later in identifying other five-sided plane figures as pentagons (Figure 2).

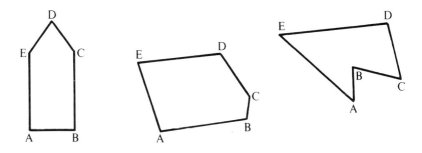

Figure 2

And what about the shape in Figure 3?

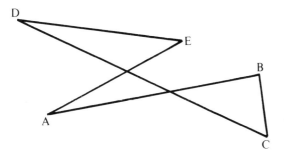

Figure 3

2.6   Confusion may arise when orientation or position changes the meaning in some cases but not in others: a square is a square whatever its position and does not become a different shape (diamond) when it is turned round, whereas 16 is not the same as 91. Another source of confusion occurs when a word in common use, for example 'similar', is given a special meaning in mathematics.

Objective 2
Remembering notation

2.7   Notation is the symbolism used in mathematics to express an idea precisely and in a shortened form: number notation, the signs for number operations, algebraic notation and formulae are important examples. This conciseness is one of the major strengths of mathematics, but it can also be a source of difficulty for many pupils. A statement such as '8 + 5 = 13' may appear to be simple but it is really a concise statement based on some complex concepts. It is damaging to pupils' mathematical development if they are rushed into the use of notation before the underlying concepts are sufficiently developed and understood. At all stages the teacher needs to stress the translation of words into mathematical symbols, and the reverse, so that pupils may develop a facility in the use of symbols and an understanding of the meanings attached to them. 'What does that mean?' should be a frequent question in all lessons at all stages.

Objective 3
Remembering conventions

2.8   Conventions are agreed ways of communicating information unambiguously without further explanation. Standard units of measurement are nationally or internationally agreed conventions. By convention numbers on the horizontal axis of a graph which lie to the right of the vertical axis are positive and those to the left are negative. In a calculation such as 4 + 3 × 2 the convention is that multiplication takes precedence over addition so that the result is 10, not 14. Aim 1 (communication) permeates all mathematics but it is particularly relevant to objectives 1 to 3. *Unless terms, notations and conventions are understood, remembered, and used frequently, consistently and in context, pupils will be unable to communicate mathematical information effectively, or to make sense of what they receive whether orally, visually or in written or printed form.*

Objective 4
Remembering results

2.9   Results are the outcome of mathematical activities. They include number bonds (or tables), formulae such as that for the area of a rectangle, the sum of the angles or a triangle, Pythagoras' Theorem . . . If pupils know some results then they may be able to deduce others from them: for example, if a pupil needs to use 5 + 6 but has forgotten the result it can be easily deduced from 5 + 5 because it is one more. The development of such an awareness saves pupils from having to remember too many facts or becoming worried by slips of memory. It is important that pupils realise that results are not arbitrary but form part of the structure of mathematics. Remembering results is helped by frequent use, but if some pupils have undue difficulty in remembering them this should not necessarily become a barrier to progress. In particular, those pupils in secondary schools who are unable to remember all the commonly known number facts should not be restricted to a narrow mathematical content consisting mainly of repetitive mechanical exercises; widespread availability of calculators has removed any need that there may have been in the past for this restriction.

B. SKILLS
(Objectives 5–9)

"Skills include not only the use of the number facts and the standard computational procedures of arithmetic and algebra, but also of any well established procedures which it is possible to carry out by the use of routine. They need not only to be understood and embedded in the conceptual structure but also to be brought up to the level of immediate recall or fluency of performance by regular practice." (*Mathematics counts*, para. 240).

Objective 5
Performing basic operations

2.10   The basic operations include not only those in number but also, at an appropriate level, algebraic operations such as solving equations and factorising. To perform the calculation 34 + 68 pupils would use some basic facts such as 4 + 8 = 12 but they would also need to understand the concept of place value and to have arithmetical skills in order to complete the calculation. Operations which at an early stage pupils would do on paper might later become mental exercises, although different methods might be used. Thus, for example, the above calculation might have been done mentally in two stages: 34 + 60 = 94; 94 + 8 = 102. At various points in this document comments are made about the undesirability of overemphasising the practising and testing of skills out of context; the ability to carry out operations is important but there is a danger that

11

skills come to be seen as ends in themselves. If mathematics is only about 'computational skills out of context' it cannot be justified as a subject in the curriculum.

Objective 6
Sensible use of a calculator

2.11 There are skills in using a calculator which need to be taught and learnt. A policy of 'allowing pupils to use a calculator' is not sufficient. What is needed is a school policy which encourages pupils of all ages and abilities to use calculators in appropriate situations and provides clear guidance on the procedures needed to obtain maximum benefit from their use. In particular, attention needs to be given to the estimation, accuracy and interpretation of results. If there is only one operation involved the procedure is obvious, but where there is more than one operation the procedures to be used on the calculator must be considered; for example the calculation of anything of the form $a/(b + c)$ needs careful handling. The use of calculators affects what might be considered appropriate under Objective 5: *only very basic and simple calculations need now be done on paper;* some standard written methods of calculation, such as long division, which many pupils find difficult and few really understand, should no longer be generally taught. To use a calculator only to check written calculations is inappropriate but to use mental or simple written approximations to check results obtained from a calculator is sensible. Logarithms, as aids to calculation, are obviously redundant.

Objective 7
Simple practical skills in mathematics

2.12 Measurement is a practical activity and pupils need to acquire skills both in using everyday measures, such as spans or cupfuls, and also in making use of a variety of standard measuring instruments. Practice in measuring is normally provided for younger pupils, but there is evidence from the work of the Assessment of Performance Unit (APU) and other sources which indicates that measuring skills among older pupils are often deficient and reveal a serious lack of appropriate experience.

2.13   *There is a danger of artificiality, even in practical activities in mathematics lessons,* as pupils are often set measuring tasks for which they see no purpose. Within normal mathematics lessons it is possible to devise activities in which the measurement of objects is the first essential step in producing data for further exploration. Other school subjects, such as home studies/home economics, science, art and craft, craft design and technology, where it is necessary to measure accurately provide excellent opportunities for the development of these skills in appropriate contexts.

Objective 8
Ability to communicate mathematics

2.14   Young children learn to understand and use the spoken word before learning to write. In many situations in life oral communication predominates. It is therefore necessary from the beginning that pupils should talk about mathematical ideas. But oral skills in mathematics among older pupils are often neglected in schools as pupils are expected to play a more passive, listening role. Writing about mathematics is not generally developed. There is a lot of 'written work' connected with 'exercises' but there is little communication of mathematical ideas in writing. An explanation of a result, a description of methods used in solving a problem or carrying out an investigation, an interpretation of a graph, or a written mathematical topic arising from an in-depth study, are among the written tasks which could feature in mathematics. Communication can be enhanced by visual presentation through the use of models, diagrams, charts and graphs, but care is needed as information can also be distorted by such a presentation. Moreover, pupils need to be able to extract, appraise and use mathematical information not only from textbooks and workcards but also from a range of other sources such as topic books, reference books, advertisements, catalogues, newspapers, radio and television.

Objective 9
The use of microcomputers in mathematical activities

2.15   Microcomputers can be used in, at least, three ways which often overlap:

(a) as a teaching aid;

(b) as a learning resource for the pupils;

(c) as a tool for the pupils to use in doing mathematical tasks.

2.16   Although each of the first two has a place in mathematical education it is the third aspect to which the objective refers. This will cover the use of a wide range of software of an open-ended nature in which the pupils have considerable control over the nature of their responses. But it will also involve an element of programming as the pupils learn to turn to the microcomputer as the most appropriate means for tackling a particular task. Work of this kind is possible with pupils aged 5 to 16 of widely differing abilities: for example, using LOGO many children of infant age and many pupils of low ability in secondary schools can program a microcomputer to produce their own designs such as that shown in Figure 4.

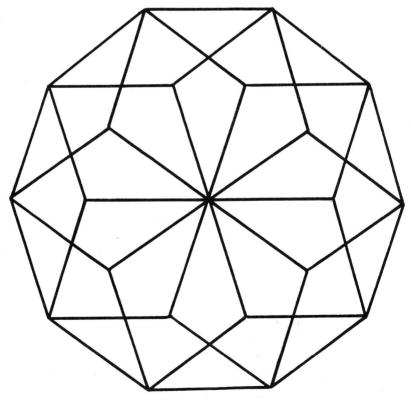

Figure 4

C. CONCEPTUAL STRUCTURES
(Objectives 10–14)

"Conceptual structures are richly interconnecting bodies of knowledge, including the routines required for the exercise of skills. It is these which make up the substance of mathematical knowledge stored in the longterm memory. They underpin the performance of skills and their presence is shown by the ability to remedy a memory failure or to adapt a procedure to a new situation." (*Mathematics counts*, para. 240).

Objective 10
Understanding basic concepts

2.17 The mastery of a skill usually requires exercises of the same kind to be repeated often. The development of a concept requires a variety of experiences in which the concept is present in some form. There is a danger that exercises leading to the mastery of skills will be overemphasised and that experiences required for the understanding of concepts will be under-played. This is one of the reasons why statements are frequently made of the kind 'they could have done the question if they had known it was on simultaneous equations'. That is, they had the skill to solve the simultaneous equations but they did not have the understanding to see that that was the skill to use.

Objective 11
The relationships between concepts

2.18 The term 'conceptual structures' is significant: it empha-sises not only the importance of concepts but also that they are within a structure in which they are inter-related. *This notion of structure* is an essential feature of mathematics at all levels. No concept stands alone: for example, subtraction is linked with addition, multiplication is linked with addition and divison, percentages are linked with fractions and decimals. In fact, each concept is linked with many other aspects of mathematics. Sometimes only the most obvious links are indi-cated, but others also need to be pointed out. Indeed, being 'good at mathematics' is dependent upon the ability to recog-nise relationships between one concept and another. In teach-ing, care needs to be taken to avoid creating false links in the minds of pupils. For example, if area and perimeter are considered together pupils may confuse them and form the wrong assumption that area is directly dependent on perimeter.

15

To correct such wrong assumptions, counter examples can be quite effective; the figures below have equal areas (6 cm²) but different perimeters (14, 10, 12 cm).

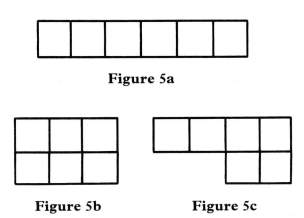

Figure 5a

Figure 5b   **Figure 5c**

Objective 12
Selecting appropriate data

2.19   Textbook problems are usually contrived so as to contain the exact amount of data needed for their solution. More realistic problems often contain either too much or too little data; for example, in biology when considering a habitat pupils have usually to handle may different pieces of data only some of which are needed for a particular mathematical analysis. Similarly if pupils are asked to plan a family holiday on a fixed budget they will have too little data initially but, having obtained a variety of travel brochures, will reach the stage of having too much data and will need to select that which is useful and appropriate.

Important mathematical experiences are provided by activities which involve the collection and selection or rejection of data and which lead to several possible solutions of a problem or to the conclusion that they cannot be solved from the data available.

Objective 13
Using mathematics in context

2.20   As already indicated in Objective 10 conceptual understanding is most effectively developed through the use of mathematics in a variety of contexts. The context might be *a practical task* which needs to be done: find the amount of grass seed required to sow a lawn; measure, cut and fit a pane of glass into a frame; check a bill; make a household budget; complete a timesheet; make a model house; analyse an advertisement; interpret information presented in the media. Or more generally the context might be *any need perceived by the pupils:* a practical classroom activity, an investigation, a game or puzzle, work in another subject in the curriculum or a topic of interest. Indeed *an exploration of a mathematical concept itself* might be the context: for example, using the skill of multiplication in a number of examples might lead to an awareness of the commutative property of multiplication (axb = bxa).

Objective 14
Interpreting results

2.21 The *validity* (or appropriateness) of any results as well as their *accuracy* should be checked. One reason is that the direct application of a mathematical skill may not give an appropriate solution to a particular practical problem. For example, the answer to $311 \div 6$ may be written as 51 remainder 5, or $51\frac{5}{6}$ or 51.83, but in a given context none of these answers might be acceptable: if there are 311 eggs then the number of half-dozen boxes required is 52, but the number of half-dozens to be sold is 51. Similarly the roots of an equation which has arisen in solving a problem need to be considered to see whether they are acceptable in terms of the practical situation from which the equation arose. Any visual representation of results such as a diagram, chart or graph, is incomplete without some interpretation. As a general rule *no result in mathematics should be accepted uncritically without asking whether it is a reasonable statement to make in the context of the question.* It is also important that pupils develop the same critical approach to information presented in the media and in advertisements.

D. GENERAL STRATEGIES
(Objectives 15–22)

"General Strategies are procedures which guide the choice of which skills to use or what knowledge to draw upon at each stage in the course of solving a problem or carrying out an investigation. They enable a problem to be approached with confidence and with the expectation that a solution will be possible." (*Mathematics counts*, para. 240).

Objective 15
Ability to estimate

2.22   Estimation is the exercise of judgment based on previous experience of number and measurement. Pupils learn to estimate the number of people in a room without counting them or to estimate the length of the room without measuring it; this ability comes through extensive experience of counting and measuring. The ability to estimate is an important general strategy in mathematics that needs to be developed through the years 5–16. It is used by a seven year old who is trying to find which block is needed to complete a model bridge; it is used by a teenager who is learning to drive a motor cycle and needs to estimate the speed of an oncoming car. It is often the first strategy to be used in mathematical activities where size is an important factor whether these occur in mathematics lessons, in other aspects of the curriculum, or in adult life.

Objective 16
Ability to approximate

2.23   Approximations are made in work involving number and measurement. Before carrying out arithmetical calculations it is useful to know the approximate value of an answer. For example, the answer to 26 × 27 must be greater than 400 (20 × 20) but less than 900 (30 × 30). Pupils should be encouraged to write in an approximate answer before using a calculator. Many pupils find it difficult to approximate in this way but if it were emphasised more when working with calculators their performance would improve. An ability to approximate is likely to be of lasting value and of general applicability in many situations.

2.24   Pupils need to recognise *the approximate nature of all measurement* even though, as their skills of measurement develop and they are able to use more refined instruments, the precision of their measurements will improve. In some contexts consideration might be given to *the degree of accuracy of results* obtained when carrying out calculations which involve measurements. If, for example, the side of a square tile is 15.0 cm (correct to one decimal place) and 20 of these tiles are placed together on a bathroom floor in a straight line then the total length, ignoring any gap between two adjacent tiles, will be between 299 cm (14.95 × 20) and 301 cm (15.05 × 20). That is, there would be a difference of 2 cm between the possible minimum and maximum lengths. Such uncertainty is evident in practice in many real situations.

Objective 17
Trial and error methods

2.25 Trial and error methods are often necessary when attempting investigations or solving problems. Such methods may lead to a clarification of what is required. For example, a task such as 'You have an arrangement of six squares cut as a whole out of a sheet of paper. Can it be folded to make a cube? What other arrangements would fold to make

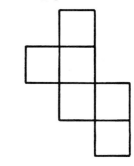

Figure 6

a cube?' initially requires a trial and error approach. Then a more systematic method must be used in order to find all the possible solutions.

2.26 In some cases successive trials may be needed in order to get closer to a solution. If, for example, it is necessary to find the length of the side of a cube whose volume is 10 cm³, the initial approximation is that it lies between 2 cm and 3 cm (as $2^3 = 8$ and $3^3 = 27$) and, clearly, it is nearer to 2 cm than it is to 3 cm. Using successive approximations the following results are obtained. As $2.1^3 = 9.261$ and $2.2^3 = 10.648$, it must lie between 2.1 cm and 2.2 cm. As $2.15^3 = 9.938375$ and $2.16^3 = 10.077696$, it must lie between 2.15 cm and 2.16 cm. And so the process could be continued. The number of successive approximations will depend on the nature of the problem and the degree of accuracy required. There is often no need to employ sophisticated techniques other than the use of the calculator, although for the most able this process may form an introduction to the study of numerical methods including their application to the solution of equations. Such

19

approaches enable pupils to attempt to solve a wider range of problems than would otherwise be possible.

Objective 18
Simplifying difficult tasks

2.27 Pupils faced with a complex design such as Figure 7a and asked how many squares there are in the figure may not be able to respond immediately, especially if they are to find the total number of squares, not just those of unit area. If they simplify the task and begin by analysing a diagram such as Figure 7b they may be able to build up, step by step, a solution to the original question. This is a general strategy of importance in tackling complicated tasks (Aims 5 and 6).

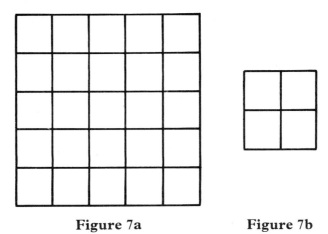

Figure 7a   **Figure 7b**

Objective 19
Looking for pattern

2.28 Pattern may be described as 'regularity of behaviour'. In mathematics, which is permeated by patterns, pupils must be encouraged to look for them. Within the curriculum 5 to 16, patterns occur in number, measurement, statistics, shape and algebra. Sometimes these patterns may produce interesting visual effects such as in the colouring of multiples on a hundred square or in the graphical representation of the scores obtained from the throwing of two dice. Generally the patterns are expressed in terms of relationships: for example, the sum of two odd numbers is an even number; the product $(x - y)(x + y)$ is $x^2 - y^2$ whatever the values of x and y; or the area of a rectangle can be calculated from the product of the length and the breadth. *Recognising, remembering and using mathematical patterns can simplify many tasks at all levels* and so form part of an important general strategy.

Objective 20
Reasoning

2.29   Reasoning is a fundamental ability which pupils need at all stages in mathematics. It is basically of the form, 'if A then B', although it is not expressed in this theoretical way for the majority of pupils. For example, pupils use their reasoning abilities when they make the following deductions:

if John is 10 years old and Mary is two years older, then Mary is 12 years old;

if John is taller than Mary and Mary is taller than Peter then John is taller than Peter;

if two angles of a triangle are 60° and 100°, then the third angle is 20°;

if $(x - 1)(x + 10) = 0$ then either $x = 1$ or $x = -10$.

2.30   Frequently when pupils cannot complete a task involving logical deduction it is not because they cannot do the separate stages but rather because they are unable to link them together. Teacher intervention often provides these links, but it is important that such intervention is designed to develop the reasoning abilities of the pupils by helping them to see the links rather than just telling them what to do.

Objective 21
Making and testing hypotheses

2.31   'Making and testing hypotheses' is often thought of as a general strategy of importance only for more able, older pupils. However, it is important at all levels. It occurs whenever a pupil says 'I think it is true that . . .' or 'If I do this then that will happen'. In fact, many general features of mathematics might be approached in this way. Does the order matter in additions such as $8 + 6$, $16 + 49 + 84$ . . .? Does the order matter in calculations such as $8 \times 2 + 4$, $8 - 2 + 4$ . . .? The

21

most popular drink of pupils in primary schools is . . .? In tossing two coins the result might be two heads, two tails or a head and a tail . . . is the chance of each of these possibilities $\frac{1}{3}$ or is it $\frac{1}{4}$ for two heads, $\frac{1}{4}$ for two tails and $\frac{1}{2}$ for a head and a tail? Do most young people watch Top of the Pops? The initial response to each of these questions might be a hypothesis which pupils can then test and discuss. In some cases alternative hypotheses might be considered. For example, the hypothesis that 'regular pentagons tessellate' can be shown to be invalid because gaps are left when an attempt is made to fit them together (Figure 8a), but a fresh hypothesis might be made to the effect that 'some pentagons tessellate' and this is valid (Figure 8b). *Making, testing and modifying hypotheses are parts of the thinking processes of everyone at different levels within mathematics, within the whole curriculum and in everyday life.*

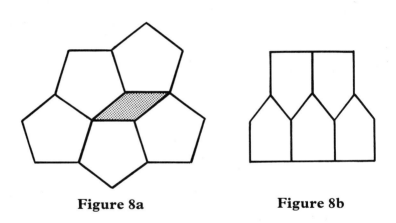

Figure 8a   Figure 8b

Objective 22
Proving and disproving

2.32   Objectives on looking for pattern (19), reasoning (20) and making and testing hypotheses (21) often result in generalisations and these need to be proved. 'Proof' is again a general strategy which might be used to varying degrees at all levels. There will be differences of opinion about what should be accepted as proof. When a young child takes two objects and then another two objects to give four objects this is, certainly to that pupil, the 'proof' that $2 + 2 = 4$. On the other hand the generalisation that the sum of two odd numbers is an even number may be 'verified' in the minds of the pupils by means of a large number of examples but verification does not constitute a proof even though nothing more rigorous might be required at that stage. When pupils realise that all odd numbers may be represented as in Figure 9a and can be put together to form an even number as in Figure 9b, they have produced a form of proof.

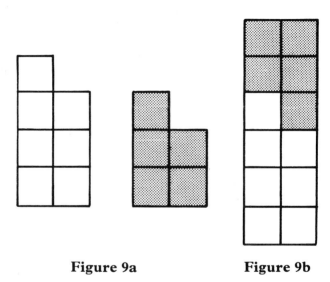

Figure 9a   **Figure 9b**

2.33   A subsequent stage is to express the proof algebraically; $(2m + 1) + (2n + 1) = 2(m + n + 1)$. The use of counter-examples is an important aspect of the general strategy of 'proving and disproving'. For example, the hypothesis that 'if a number is multiplied by another number then that number is always increased' is disproved if it is multiplied by 1 (or 0 or $\frac{1}{2}$). Counter examples can be used not only in this way to disprove a hypothesis but also to give fresh insights and understanding. For example, on the basis of Figure 10a, a hypothesis might be made that the sides of a quadrilateral can be cut by a straight line in no more than two points

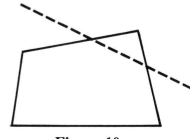

Figure 10a

(unless the sides are produced). But in questioning this statement we might reflect on the nature of a quadrilateral and arrive at Figure 10b where the sides of a (concave) quadrilateral can be cut by a straight line in four points.

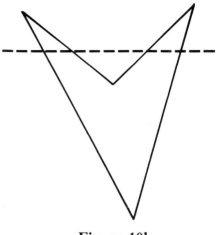

Figure 10b

E. PERSONAL QUALITIES
(Objectives 23, 24)

2.34   Each of the objectives already considered makes a contribution, whether direct or indirect, to the development of desirable personal qualities, especially if the content of the mathematics curriculum and the classroom approaches used are appropriate (Chapters 3 and 4). Nevertheless, the checklist of objectives would be incomplete without the following objectives which refer specifically to these personal qualities. *It must not be assumed that these objectives relate only to older, more able pupils as they are, in fact, achievable by pupils of all ages and abilities within appropriate contexts.* They ought to be given high priority.

Objective 23
Good work habits

2.35   In order that pupils may reach the standards of which they are capable in Objectives 1-22 they must develop good work habits in mathematics such as those described in the aims, of being:

imaginative, creative, flexible;
systematic;
independent in thought and action;
cooperative;
persistent;

To achieve success in each aspect it is essential that the classroom approaches (Chapter 4) are designed so as to foster its development.

Objective 24
A positive attitude to mathematics

"The extent to which the need to undertake even an apparently simple and straightforward piece of mathematics could induce feelings of anxiety, helplessness, fear and even guilt in some of those interviewed was, perhaps, the most striking feature of the study." (*Mathematics counts*, para. 20).

2.36 The study referred to in this quotation is described in the the report *Use of mathematics by adults in daily life* by Bridgid Sewell. This and other findings reveal a widespread, negative attitude to mathematics among adults. It is necessary to take action to encourage a more positive attitude made up of the following features:

fascination with the subject;

interest and motivation;

pleasure and enjoyment from mathematical activities;

appreciation of the purpose, power and relevance of mathematics;

satisfaction derived from a sense of achievement;

confidence in an ability to do mathematics at an appropriate level.

2.37 The fostering of such positive attitudes is important throughout the years 5-16 and all teachers need to give it careful attention:

"During every mathematics lesson a child is not only learning, or failing to learn, mathematics as a result of the work he is doing but is also developing his attitude towards mathematics. In every mathematics lesson his teacher is conveying, even if unconsciously, a message about mathematics which will influence this attitude. Once attitudes have been formed, they can be very persistent and difficult to change. Positive attitudes assist the learning of mathematics; negative attitudes not only inhibit learning but . . . very often persist into adult life and affect choice of job." (*Mathematics counts*, para. 345).

25

3. Criteria for content

3.1 This chapter is concerned with the criteria which might determine the content of the mathematics curriculum. It must be possible to say why a particular item is included and how it might be approached, but these criteria do not stand alone. They should be seen in conjunction with the aims and objectives already described in Chapters 1 and 2 respectively and also in conjunction with the classroom approaches to be described in Chapter 4.

3.2 As indicated in the Introduction, *Mathematics counts* is essential reading for all concerned with mathematics in the curriculum. As such it relates directly to every aspect of this document and it has certainly much to say about the content of mathematics teaching. In particular, useful advice is given on the policy to be followed in deciding on the appropriateness of content.

"Development should be 'from the bottom upwards' by considering the range of work which is appropriate for lower-attaining pupils and extending this range as the level of attainment of pupils increases. In this way it should be possible to ensure both that pupils are not required to tackle work which is inappropriate to their level of attainment and, equally importantly, that those who are capable of going a long way are enabled to do so." (*Mathematics counts*, para. 450).

3.3 *Mathematical content needs to be differentiated to match the abilities of the pupils* but, according to the principle quoted from the Cockcroft Report, this is achieved at each stage through extensions rather than deletions. This is a positive approach to a differentiated curriculum based more on what pupils can do than on what they cannot do: more on pupils' successes than on their failures. Viewed in this way a differentiated curriculum does not act like a straitjacket on pupils' progress; just the reverse: as pupils show what they can do they can then progress as far and as rapidly as their abilities will allow. *Differentiation of content, if well planned, facilitates progression for all pupils.*

3.4 This approach to the choice of mathematical content cannot be over-emphasised, but it must be properly understood. It does not mean that pupils will not be challenged. In fact, it is important that *all pupils should be challenged* whatever their age or ability, but not challenged beyond reasonable limits: *challenge which does not usually lead to success is counterproductive.*

3.5   *Differentiation within the mathematics curriculum is, however, a complex issue involving more than differentiation of content, being related also to the contexts of the mathematical activity, to the complexity of language used, to the type of resources and to the classroom approaches.* At one extreme there may be aspects of mathematics, such as number operations on whole numbers, in which there might be no difference in content between the ages of 11 and 16 for the majority of pupils (see Appendix 1), but there would be a considerable difference in the contexts considered and in the resources used to suit the different levels of maturity of the pupils. In particular, textbook or workcard materials which are well suited to the needs of pupils in primary schools are not, in general, suitable for 15 year olds even if these are low attainers. On the other hand the same investigative activity (Chapter 4, principle 10) might be used with a wide range of ages and abilities, even though it would be presented in different ways for different groups of pupils, and the resulting work could differ considerably in terms of content. For example, pupils might be asked to examine the volumes of open boxes made by cutting equal squares from the corners of a square sheet of paper and folding as shown in Figures 11a and b (see Appendix 2).

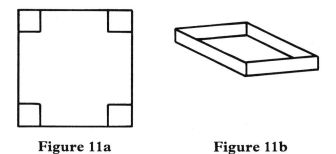

Figure 11a   **Figure 11b**

3.6   At a low level, making such a box and finding its volume would be a major achievement. But at a higher level pupils would be expected to find which squares cut from the corners would produce the largest volume and perhaps to extend the investigation to consider closed boxes or the use of rectangular sheets of paper which are not square. The value of an activity of this kind is that *the differentiation is determined largely by*

27

*the abilities of the pupils and their achievements within the activity
itself and is not pre-determined by the teacher.*

3.7   The decisions which have to be made about mathematical
content in relation to the differing needs of all pupils from 5
to 16 should be governed by the criteria that follow.

Criterion 1
Mathematical content needs to be chosen so that the pupils for whom it is intended can cover it successfully at their own appropriate level

3.8   At present the desire 'to cover the syllabus' creates problems for the teacher as the syllabus often contains so much
that even superficial coverage, let alone thorough coverage, is
impossible for many pupils. This kind of pressure is felt even
in the primary years, particularly just before pupils transfer to
the next stage of education. In the secondary years leading up
to examinations at 16-plus the pressure is most intense. The
result is often a mixture of failure, lack of confidence, anxiety
and dislike of mathematics by the pupils. This is not to say
that, whatever their ages or abilities, pupils should not be
challenged, but the challenge has to be posed in such a way
that they generally meet with success and make progress. In
any redesigning of a mathematics syllabus the choice of content
should enable it to be covered thoroughly in such a way that
the aims and objectives are realistic and can be achieved.
Nothing should be included for which there is not a sound,
clearly defined purpose, understood and appreciated by the
pupils. In particular, there is no point in including an item
where the only objective which pupils can achieve with confidence is the manipulation of numbers or other symbols out of
context. For example, for most pupils the division of one
fraction by another, the multiplication of matrices and the
solution of quadratic equations will never have any relevance.
In recent decades genuine attempts to enrich the mathematical
experiences of the pupils have often depended on the introduction of items of new content, some of which could not be
developed beyond a trivial level with many pupils. It is vitally
important to provide a rich mathematical experience but this
will often come, not just from the composition of the content,
but more particularly from the nature of the classroom
approaches (Chapter 4).

Criterion 2
Mathematical content should not be so extensive that it imposes restrictions on the range of classroom approaches
(see Chapter 4)

3.9   The pressure to cover the syllabus is often given as the reason for curtailing discussion and not including practical work, investigative activity and problem solving as these are more time-consuming than formal methods. To ensure that these and other approaches to the teaching and learning of mathematics, which are essential to the full development of pupils' mathematical abilities, can be implemented is another reason for some reductions in the present content. A reduction in content will enable teachers to make better provision for the achievement of the stated objectives and of those aims which relate directly to the development of personal qualities.

Criterion 3
Mathematical content should form a coherent structure

3.10   Whatever the age or ability of the pupils, the content should not be a collection of largely unconnected items. Instead it should be designed as a structure in which the various parts relate together coherently. It is not just that one item is related to another item, but rather that there is a whole network of relationships. It is important that mathematics guidelines should stress whichever relationships are appropriate at each stage and that teaching approaches should exploit them (see Chapter 4, principle 3). The aim is that all pupils should acquire some appreciation of the *structure* of the mathematics they have done and understand the relationships between particular concepts.

Criterion 4
Mathematical content should be sufficiently broad for all pupils

3.11   Reducing the content of the mathematics curriculum need not result in less breadth for any pupils. In particular it is most important that pupils of low attainment are not restricted to a purely arithmetical diet taught in a narrow way; there must be sufficient breadth to enable a network of content to

29

be established in the pupils' minds. Mathematics for all pupils, including the low attainers, should certainly include a considerable geometrical component with work in both two and three dimensions aimed to develop their spatial thinking. Algebraic ideas can also emerge in the work of most pupils in contexts where the need to make concise statements arises naturally. In fact, there are many mathematical activities in which numerical, geometrical and algebraic elements come together in a natural way. The statement that 'a square number may be written symbolically as n^2' is a simple illustration of this point. These numbers may be represented visually by counters or dots arranged in squares:

Figure 12

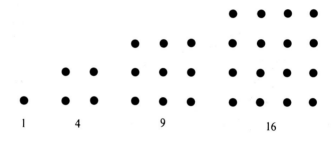

When pupils say that, for example, the twelfth square number is 12^2 they are beginning to express themselves algebraically even before they express it as n^2. However, there is no point in creating artificial algebraic exercises for low attainers such as numerical substitutions in meaningless formulae or the simplification of expressions through collecting 'like' terms.

Criterion 5
Mathematical content should meet the mathematical needs of the rest of the curriculum

3.12   The mathematical needs of the whole curriculum provide excellent opportunities for placing mathematics in context. The main content needs are as follows: basic properties of number and number operations; the use of calculators; measurement; approximation and estimation; the use of ready reckoners; the use of charts, diagrams and graphs; statistics (collection, representation and interpretation of data); ratio and proportion; the use of formulae; elementary geometry of two and three dimensions. In secondary schools where the teaching is mainly within subject departments, there needs to be considerable staff consultation and planning to develop common policies relating to many of the objectives described in Chapter 2. These will include cooperation between departments on such matters as subject-specific examples to be used in mathematics and vice versa, together with some agreement on their timing. Where the use of class teachers is the norm, as in primary schools, it is the responsibility of each individual teacher to ensure that mathematics is used where appropriate opportunities occur. At all levels there should be a positive approach to the wide use of mathematics throughout the curriculum. If mathematics is not seen to be needed or used explicitly in project work and in other subjects within the curriculum then the claim that mathematics is a useful subject must sound rather hollow to the pupils.

Criterion 6
Mathematical content should meet the basic mathematical needs of adult life, including employment

3.13   At present all pupils by the age of 16 will have followed a mathematics curriculum which includes all the basic mathematical content required in adult life. Unfortunately, many pupils who will not need anything more will have covered that content very inadequately. In redesigning the mathematics syllabus for all pupils these basic mathematical needs of adult life should be given much greater emphasis than now. The Cockcroft Report summarises these needs as follows:

". . . the ability to read numbers and to count, to tell the time, to pay for purchases and to give change, to weigh and measure, to understand straightforward timetables and simple graphs and charts and to carry out any necessary calculations associated with these." (*Mathematics counts*, para. 32).

". . . It is important to have the feeling for number which permits sensible estimation and approximation. . ." (*Ibid,* para. 33).

"Although estimation is important, counting and measurement are paramount. A very great deal of the mathematics used in employment is concerned with measurement in one or other of a wide variety of forms, by no means all of which are directly concerned with the use of measuring instruments." (*Ibid,* para. 79).

31

Care must be taken to ensure that, whenever appropriate, mathematics is taught in context.

Criterion 7

Mathematical content should include elements which are intrinsically interesting and important

3.14 The utilitarian aspect of mathematics is important but if narrowly interpreted it can be counter-productive, stifling the mathematical development of the pupils. The impression should not be given that everything that is done ought to be directly relevant either to another subject or to some area of adult life. There is much that is intrinsically interesting and important in itself: for example, number patterns and sequences, magic squares, modular arithmetic, geometrical patterns, properties of geometric shapes in two and three dimensions, topology. Even if such elements might not appear to be directly relevant to everyday life, the experience provided for the pupils is essential to the full development of their mathematical abilities. An item of interest which might appear to have little practical significance may have a greater usefulness than is often realised. For example, the construction of a solid from one piece of card (called 'the net of the solid') is relevant to the production of containers of all kinds: Figure 13a shows a possible net of what might be a box of cereals (Figure 13b). Applicants for sheet metal apprenticeships are

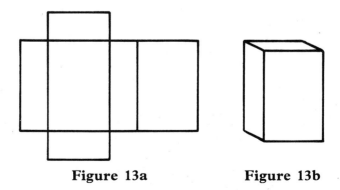

Figure 13a   **Figure 13b**

known to be shown by one firm a variety of hollow cones and asked to draw the shapes of the pieces of metal which would be required to make them.

Criterion 8
In choosing mathematical content appropriate weighting should be given to key aspects

3.15 Aims 1 to 3 are expressed in terms of the essential nature of mathematics and the content will need to reflect clearly each of these aspects: mathematics as a means of communication (Aim 1), mathematics as a tool (Aim 2) and the relationships within mathematics (Aim 3). Some specific items of content are of crucial importance. For example, it is impossible to make any progress in mathematics without a sound grasp of place value and the whole decimal notation. It is also impossible to progress without understanding the nature of the number operations of addition, subtraction, multiplication and division, although with the availability of calculators it is possible to make progress without remembering many number facts and without mastering written methods of performing these operations. *It may be appropriate to distinguish here between what is essential and what is desirable* (or even highly desirable). If pupils forget that $7 \times 9 = 63$ how serious is it? It would be very serious indeed if they did not understand the meaning of 63. But failing to recall the number fact itself is much less serious if the pupil can easily find the answer from first principles or, if necessary, from a reference table or from a calculator. Failure to understand place value could not be so easily remedied. The view of what is essential depends on the abilities of the pupils: the foundation list of *Mathematics counts* (para. 458) is essential for all pupils at 16, but as is said in that report much more than that should be expected of more able pupils. *Decisions on priorities within the content of mathematics must be taken by schools on the basis of their earlier decisions about the priorities within the objectives.*

Criterion 9
Mathematical content should take account of the potential of electronic calculators

3.16 The significance for mathematics of the fact that cheap electronic calculators enable the basic number operations to be performed instantly by the pressing of a few buttons has not yet been fully realised. For example, there is no longer any need for pupils to be held back if they are unable, in spite of long, frustratingly unsuccessful attempts, to master these operations. Raw data, however complex, can now be handled

33

so easily that mathematics can be given a greater sense of reality in what is done. The solution of a wider range of equations using numerical methods is now within the reach of many pupils. The emphasis in mathematics teaching can now be placed much more on conceptual structures and general strategies. A calculator will perform number operations accurately but will not give any help in deciding which operation to use in a particular situation; it is this latter task which is the more important and often the more difficult for pupils. Nevertheless, there is evidence to show that pupils' facility with number and their understanding of basic concepts will improve significantly if calculators are used appropriately. Contrary to some popular opinion, *calculators do not consititute a threat to mathematics education. Used sensibly they will make pupils better at mathematics, not worse.*

Criterion 10
The content should be influenced increasingly by developments in microcomputing

"The implications of current technology are so extensive that it is difficult to present a balanced appraisal without seeming to exaggerate. No doubt further developments are still to come, but whatever changes microcomputers may make to mathematical education in the future we may say, beyond all doubt, that some of the changes which they have made already are so big that we lack any previous standard by which to compare them. So far the changes in the school curriculum are small, and the changes in mathematics syllabuses are very small indeed, but in some schools changes in the methods of teaching mathematics can already be seen and these could develop rapidly. The greatest change of all, however, is in the response of the pupils." (*Microcomputers and mathematics in schools,* para. 3).

3.17 This quotation is more optimistic about the current influence of microcomputers on the approaches to the teaching and learning of mathematics than on the content itself. Nevertheless, the influence of microcomputers on content is likely to increase, and in any case content and approaches react strongly on each other. Microcomputers are a powerful means of doing mathematics extremely quickly and sometimes in a visually dramatic way. If pupils are to use microcomputers in this way they will need to learn to program the machines and so, if programming is not taught elsewhere, it should be included in mathematics lessons. For mathematical purposes such programming does not need to be highly sophisticated. It may be a form of LOGO, or the early stages of a language such as BASIC, or indeed any form of computer control which enables pupils to carry out their own mathematical activities. Having acquired such skill the pupils may use it to study in greater depth items of mathematical content which are considered important, for example, the properties of numbers, the representation and analysis of data, and the spatial relationships in geometrical figures.

4. Classroom approaches

4.1   If the aims and objectives of mathematics adopted by a school are as broad as those proposed in Chapters 1 and 2 respectively, and if the content is determined not in an arbitrary way but as a result of using important criteria as proposed in Chapter 3, the effects on classroom approaches to the teaching and learning of mathematics will be considerable. The approach to be adopted in any particular instance will depend on the topic to be taught and will need to be related to the abilities and experiences of the pupils. In this chapter consideration is given to important principles which should govern these approaches so that the aims and objectives might be achieved. The total effect should be an appreciation by the pupils of mathematics as a living process in which all can be involved.

Principle 1
Needs perceived by the pupils

4.2   New content is generally introduced because it follows, or appears to follow, logically from what has gone before. But the pupils are not always fully aware of the need for such progression. As a general principle any move into new content should occur when the need for it has been made clear in the work being done by the pupils, perhaps within an activity or a problem which cannot be tackled without it. For example, in measurement small units such as a millimetre should be introduced when there is a need for greater precision in what the pupils are doing; negative numbers should be introduced when a need to extend the number system emerges, say, in work in temperature, or height relative to sea level, or in

35

graphical work. The spirit of the approach is best captured by the provision of suitable experiences for the pupils in which they are challenged and encouraged to explore new ideas and called upon to devise their own techniques.

Principle 2
A firm conceptual basis

4.3   The early stages of learning mathematics are of crucial importance and should not be sacrificed because of pressure for the pupils to do written exercises as soon as possible. As a general statement about mathematics 5 to 16 this applies particularly to the important foundation work in the early years when there is a very strong temptation for schools to go for superficially quick progress in written work before the pupils' conceptual understanding is sufficiently well established. But it also applies at all levels within any mathematical topic. For example, there is something fundamentally wrong with teaching approaches which lead to pupils being able to multiply and divide without their knowing which operation to use in a particular situation. The principle suggested will appear to many to result in unacceptably slow progress, but progress in pupils' mathematical understanding is more important than progress in the performance of skills. In fact, *when the early stages of learning are firmly established subsequent progress can take place much more quickly and confidently.*

Principle 3
Flexibility

4.4   A linear model of the mathematics content (Figure 14 a) illustrates the sequencing of stages within a hierarchy. There is, of course, a strong hierarchical element in mathematics in the sense that certain prior knowledge is often necessary before something new is understood: for example, three-figure whole numbers cannot be understood unless two-figure whole numbers are also understood. However, mathematical learning does not necessarily take place in completely predetermined sequences and any assumption that it does can seriously stunt pupils' progress. The temptation already referred to of keeping low-achieving pupils indefinitely on arithmetical exercises until all number facts are known and computational skills mastered can lead to an unnecessarily restrictive curriculum for the pupils concerned. A network model (Figure 14 b) illustrates that there may be different routes from one point to another: for example, within work on the areas of plane figures there is no reason why the area of a triangle must be studied before that of a circle. Whereas the linear model suggests a static view of the mathematics curriculum, the network model suggests a dynamic view, much more reactive to pupils' progress and interests, and to the mathematical needs which may arise in particular activities. A spiral model (Figure 14 c) illustrates the recurring nature of mathematical development, where each aspect is touched on frequently and taken a stage further: for example, the square root of a number would occur in work on square numbers, the areas of squares and circles, Pythagoras' Theorem, indices, exploration of the keys of a calculator and the solution of equations. Although, as in all modelling, the different models have their own strengths and weaknesses, each of them stresses different aspects of mathematical progression in a useful way. Flexibility is needed so that these alternative strategies might be used when appropriate.

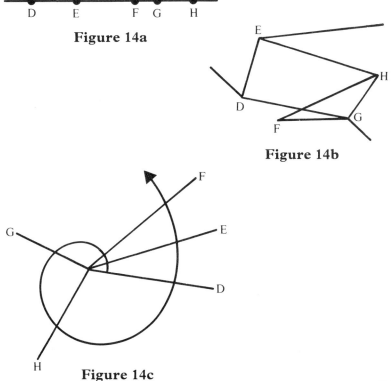

Figure 14a

Figure 14b

Figure 14c

Principle 4
Encouragement to all pupils of both sexes and of different cultural backgrounds

4.5   It is hoped that all that is proposed in this paper will make mathematics a more worthwhile experience for all pupils. In addition, specific efforts need to be made to ensure that mathematics is a less male-orientated subject than it is at present. To achieve this, there must be higher expectations of what girls can do, with more encouragement given them to participate in all activities. Greater use needs to be made of a wide range of resources and activities which reflect the interests of all; for example, home studies/home economics (involving both boys and girls) can provide useful cross-curricular links. The same principle applies to the encouragment of all pupils whatever their cultural background: for example, Islamic art is a fertile area for the exploration of geometrical design.

4.6   Principles 5 to 10 which follow refer specifically to the six activities which the Cockcroft Report said should be included in mathematics teaching at all levels (See *Mathematics counts*, paragraph 243 and those paragraphs immediately following it).

Principle 5
Exposition by the teacher

4.7   The purpose of exposition by the teacher is not that everything should be so well explained to the pupils that they become simply passive recipients of mathematics as a body of knowledge. Instead the purpose should be to stimulate and activate pupils so that, as far as possible, they reach the various objectives under their own initiative. *Successful exposition may take many different forms* but the following are some of the qualities which should be present: it challenges and provokes the pupils to think; it is reactive to pupils' needs and so it exploits questioning techniques and discussion; it is used at different points in the process of learning and so, for example, it may take the form of pulling together a variety of activities in which the pupils have been engaged; and it uses a variety of stimuli. Exposition may be given to individual pupils, a small group, a whole class and, in team teaching, to several classes together; no pupil should be restricted to only one of these approaches as each approach has its own particular strengths and weaknesses. The implementation of the principles which follow would result in less exposition in most classrooms than at present; but when it is done it needs to be done well.

Principle 6
Discussion

4.8   There is much to discuss in mathematics: the nature of a problem in order to comprehend what is intended; the relevance of the data; the strategies which might be used to produce solutions; and the concepts which need to be clarified and extended. The correctness of results needs to be discussed; where mistakes have been made these should not be ignored or summarily dismissed as they are often profitable points for discussion if handled sensitively. But useful discussion can also take place between pupils without the involvement of the teacher. This is particularly so when they are cooperating in solving a problem, involved in investigative work, carrying out a statistical survey, doing a practical task which requires more than one pupil to complete it, or working together on a micro-computer. *The quality of pupils' mathematical thinking as well as their ability to express themselves are considerably enhanced by discussion.*

Principle 7
Appropriate practical work

4.9   Practical work is of three main kinds:

(a) There is the practical work which enables pupils to understand mathematical concepts. For example, working with bundles of sticks or structural apparatus can help pupils to understand place value. Planned activities with water and containers help pupils to form the concepts of volume and capacity. Making geometrical models helps pupils to understand spatial relationships. Throwing dice helps pupils to develop an understanding of probability. Carrying out a statistical survey and analysing and interpreting the data help pupils to understand concepts such as mean, standard deviation and the various statistical distributions. There is a tendency to minimise the importance of this type of practical work at the later primary stage and at the secondary stage. Mathematics is an abstract subject and becomes almost exclusively so too quickly for many pupils. Without sufficient practical experience the pupils are unable to relate abstract mathematical concepts to any form of reality. *All pupils benefit from appropriate practical work of this kind* whatever their age or ability.

(b) There is the practical work of measurement which needs to be done with a particular purpose in mind whether as a

39

part of mathematical activities or in other subjects of the curriculum. Meaningless calculations involving measurements, such as the multiplication of 2 hours 27 minutes by 6, serve little useful purpose.

(c) The activity itself might be conducive to a practical approach. For example, most pupils would find it easier to obtain the number of cubes in this diagram (Figure 15) by doing it practically rather than performing a calculation on paper. Problem solving and investigational work will often involve some practical element.

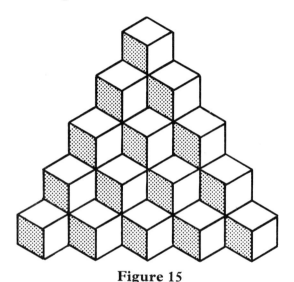

Figure 15

Principle 8
Consolidation and practice of fundamental skills

4.10   Skills need to be introduced for a perceived purpose and used in context and with understanding. However, in order that skills should be mastered provision must be made for adequate consolidation and practice. In general, short frequent practising of skills is better than long concentrated periods of practice. The former approach enables the teacher to organise lessons in such a way that each will include a variety of activities and avoid spending the whole time on skill practice. Some pupils master skills more quickly than others and the emphasis given to practising them should vary. Just as in the teaching of English attention to particular language skills is best given in the context of what the pupils have been saying or writing for real purposes and where needs have been exposed, so in the teaching of mathematics, attention to skills is best given in the context of more general mathematical activities where pupils have revealed weaknesses in the use of those skills and clearly require further consolidation and practice.

Principle 9
Problem solving

"The ability to solve problems is at the heart of mathematics."
(*Mathematics counts*, para. 249)

4.11   There are often unpleasant connotations in the general usage of the word 'problem' and, to some extent, this can carry over into mathematics lessons. But if problem solving is an essential part of mathematical activity throughout the years 5 to 16 and pupils acquire a confidence in their own abilities through tackling tasks appropriate to them, some of the apprehension often expressed by many pupils should diminish. In fact, many children entering school can already solve simple problems – having five sweets and eating three they can recognise that they have two left, although, understandably, few can do the corresponding manipulation (5 − 3). There are various sources of suitable problems: textbooks, reference books, professional journals, games and puzzles, other subjects in the curriculum, adult life and employment. But a classroom where a range of activities is taking place and in which pupils express interests and ask questions can also provide on-the-spot problems. Teachers need to exploit these situations because there is greater motivation to solve problems which have been posed by the pupils themselves. Problems should be chosen with a range of possible outcomes: some problems have a unique solution; some have no solution; others would have a solution if more information were available; many will have several solutions and the merit of each may need to be assessed. The process of starting with a real problem, abstracting and solving a corresponding mathematical problem and then checking its solutions in the practical situation is often called mathematical modelling. It is worth stressing to pupils that, in real life, mathematical solutions to problems have often to be judged by criteria of a non-mathematical nature, some of which may be political, moral or social. For example, the most direct route for a proposed new stretch of motorway might be unacceptable as it would cut across a heavily built-up area.

41

Principle 10
Investigative work

4.12   The various approaches considered in this chapter need not be isolated from each other but may all be part of the same activity. In particular, clear distinctions do not exist between problem solving and investigative work. Nevertheless in broad terms it is useful to think of problem solving as being a convergent activity where the pupils have to reach a solution to a defined problem, whereas investigative work should be seen as a more divergent activity. In an investigative approach pupils are encouraged to think of alternative strategies, to consider what would happen if a particular line of action were pursued, or to see whether certain changes would make any difference to the outcome. In fact, it might be through an investigative approach to a problem that a solution emerged; for example, if the problem is to find the most economical way to package bars of chocolate of a certain shape it would be necessary to investigate various possibilities before coming to a decision.

4.13   Of course, practical work, problem solving and investigative activities are time consuming and some schools will be concerned that their introduction will result in unsatisfactory coverage of the content of the mathematics curriculum. A

Figure 16

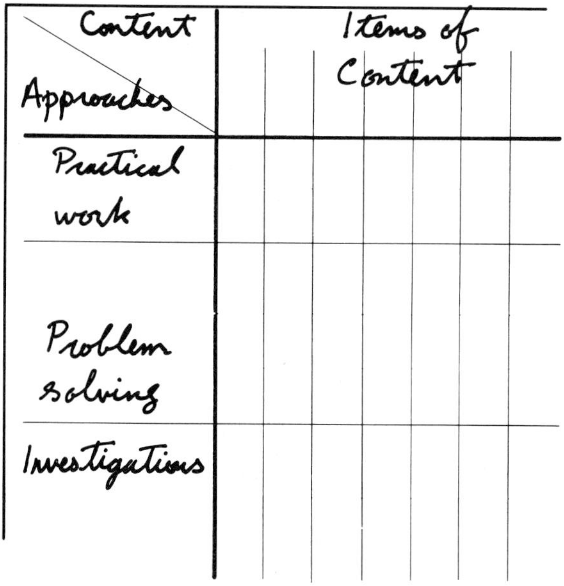

useful analysis might be made by means of a grid such as Figure 16 in which these approaches are directly related to content. This highlights at least two features: by reading across the grid the strength of the impact of particular approaches and by reading down the grid the depth of coverage of particular items of content are revealed. As a result the teachers will see more clearly where the strengths and weaknesses are and what needs to be done to ensure breadth and balance in terms of both content and classroom approaches.

Principle 11
Resources

4.14   Resources are needed which fully reflect the aims, objectives, content and classroom approaches. These will include a wide range of printed material, not only textbooks and worksheets but also supporting reference material and topic books. 'Raw material' such as catalogues, brochures, forms and publicity leaflets are especially useful for work with older pupils in relating mathematics directly to adult life. Appropriate equipment for practical work is clearly necessary at all stages. Calculators and microcomputers are essential.

4.15   Audio-visual materials can enrich many mathematical activities. The atmosphere in which mathematics is taught ought to be conducive to learning, with stimulating and attractive display of the above resources, together with the display of pupils' work and of objects and posters of interest. This is very important: whether it is the mathematics area in a classroom for seven year olds, or the mathematics room used by 15 year olds, it should be a place which attracts pupils and arouses their interests.

Principle 12
Organisational arrangements

4.16   The organisation of pupils, the deployment of staff, the writing of schemes of work and the use of resources and accommodation are important issues for all schools. Decisions that are taken should be based on the following considerations:

(a) continuity and progression should be ensured from one class or teacher to another, and from one school to another;

(b) pupils of all abilities should be able to achieve their full potential;

(c) the organisation should ensure that all pupils may experience a full range of classroom approaches;

(d) opportunities should be provided to allow pupils to work independently, to engage in cooperative activities and to pursue topics of interest in some depth;

(e) teachers and pupils should have ready access to appropriate resources;

(f) the strengths and enthusiasm of the individual members of staff should be exploited to the full.

4.17 Achieving these goals places a premium on extensive staff consultation and cooperation within schools and between schools.

5. Assessment

5.1 Assessment is perhaps the most discussed aspect of the mathematics curriculum, partly because of the national concern to define more clearly the levels of achievement reached by school pupils. Nevertheless, it is important to emphasise that assessment should develop out of the curriculum, its aims, objectives, criteria for content and approaches, and not the reverse. Neither narrow assessment techniques nor cluttered examination syllabuses at 16-plus should be allowed to distort the aims, objectives and approaches required in a mathematics curriculum which is broad, balanced, relevant and suitably differentiated.

5.2 In this chapter some principles are proposed which might be used constructively in developing school assessment policies. These principles and any resultant action by schools should be seen against the background of some recent important publications on assessment. Of particular significance are the publications of the APU which is concerned with monitoring national attainment at 11 and 15; *Children's understanding of mathematics* which contains the results of work carried out by a research team at Chelsea College; and *Mathematics counts*, which has much to say on assessment and examinations at 16-plus (see particularly Chapters 8 and 10).

5.3 Assessment records built up by a school should be comprehensive, covering the full range of objectives and showing the strengths and weaknesses of the pupils, their progress and their attitudes. Uninterpreted scores are of little value. A useful approach is to have one record sheet covering a year in the life of the pupil in which one side of the sheet contains carefully structured details of the appropriate objectives and scores on any standardised tests used, while the reverse side is used for recording pupils' progress as measured against their own previous achievements, other significant aspects such as qualitative judgments by the teacher, or unexpected developments in their performance. Particularly in the later years of the secondary school the pupils themselves might well be involved in developing their own records, or profiles, of themselves and their achievements.

5.4   Assessment is a means to an end. The end is the achievement by all pupils of a degree of mathematical competence commensurate with their abilities and needs, and the development of appropriate attitudes to the subject. It is through the aims and objectives of a sound mathematics curriculum that this end is to be achieved and assessment should be geared to measuring and recording the pupil's progress in relation to these aims and objectives. But the performance of the pupils reflects the nature of what is provided by the school and so the quality of the mathematics curriculum itself requires continuous evaluation:

(a) Are the learning experiences provided by the classroom approaches completely suitable or can they be improved?

(b) Does the content need to be amended?

(c) Do priorities within the content need to change to meet the needs of pupils and the society of the future?

(d) Is the content relevant to the information technology age?

(e) Are the aims and objectives still appropriate?

5.5   The assessment procedures themselves should not be immune from such an evaluation:

(f) Are they detrimental in their effects in any way?

(g) Do they tell pupils, teachers and others what they need to know?

(h) How are they used?

(i) How can they be improved?

5.6   An assessment policy should be based on certain important principles.

45

Principle 1
Assessment of the full range of objectives

5.7   The easiest objectives to assess are facts and skills but any assessment is inadequate if these are all that is assessed. Due attention needs to be given to the assessment of conceptual structures and general strategies because these objectives are more indicative of pupils' mathematical abilities. To ensure that these four groups of objectives are covered it is necessary for teachers to know exactly what is being assessed by a question and, more significantly, what is indicated by the answers to the question. For example, 38×9 performed on paper using the standard method requires a knowledge of multiplication facts (8×9, 3×9) and addition facts ($7 + 7$) together with the concept of place value and the skill in using these to obtain the final result. A question set in a context in which the pupils have to decide which operation to use and then to perform 38×9 reveals something about their conceptual understanding of multiplication. If pupils are encouraged to calculate 38×9 using a variety of methods they may reveal not only a knowledge of multiplication and addition facts but also a sound conceptual understanding of the task and the ability to use various strategies in performing it. For example, pupils might use any of the following methods:

$$38 \times 9 = 38 \times 3 \times 3$$
$$38 \times 9 = 38 \times 2 \times 2 \times 2 + 38$$
$$38 \times 9 = 38 \times 10 - 38$$

Moreover, each major aspect of the mathematics curriculum should also be assessed in terms of its contribution to the development of the fifth group of objectives (personal qualities).

Principle 2
Assessment of facts and skills in context

5.8   It is relatively easy to assess facts and skills out of context, but this has little value. With regard to a particular skill it is not sufficient to ask whether the pupils can perform the skill; we must also ask whether they can use it in a variety of contexts, whether they understand it and whether it has contributed to the overall development of their mathematical abilities. In particular, any statement on pupils' abilities at transfer from one class or school to another or at 16-plus should be based on the assessment of all objectives in appropriate contexts.

Principle 3
The relationship between assessment and classroom approaches

5.9   Different classroom approaches elicit a variety of responses from the pupils: oral, written and practical; and increasingly in the future their responses might be on micro-computers. The nature of the tasks which can be used in making assessments range from short items to the in-depth studies of some topics, problem solving and investigative work.

5.10   The grid illustrates a framework which could be adapted and used by schools to relate assessment procedures to the full range of classroom approaches. At present, the assessment of mathematics in the 5 to 16 age range, even in many infant or first schools, is generally based on written responses to short

Tasks / Responses	Short items	Problem solving	Investigational work	In-depth studies
Written				
Oral				
Practical				
Micro-computer				

items, as represented by the shaded area of the grid. However, where the classroom approaches are as broad as those described in Chapter 4 this assessment is inadequate. Every aspect of assessment should be effectively covered at all stages and 16-plus examinations should not be excluded from such a requirement. *It is essential that assessment should reflect broad classroom approaches to the teaching and learning of mathematics, and provide a positive stimulus to their future development.*

Principle 4
Assessment as an integral part of the teaching and learning of mathematics

5.11   At present undue importance is often attached to termly

47

or yearly tests. If these produce any major surprises for the teacher it reveals that the assessment aspect of the teaching approach is inadequate because effective teaching can only take place with continuing assessment of the pupils' responses. When the *oral element* in normal lessons is mainly discussion (with an individual, group or class), rather than exposition, the teacher is enabled to know a considerable amount about the mathematical thinking of the pupils. Assessment of the normal *written work* (including homework for older pupils) is often expressed in terms of the number of right answers, but this in itself is a limited approach and it needs to be coupled with a closer analysis of the quality of some of the work done. *Microcomputer* programs may have their own built-in forms of assessment which indicate the soundness of pupils' responses, but this type of activity is so new that this kind of assessment is still in its infancy. *Practical work* provides an excellent opportunity for the teacher to observe and assess pupils' performance and also to raise issues for discussion. Whatever the type of response, there should be an analysis of the pupils' thinking even when a right answer is achieved; pupils should be helped to find their own mistakes. A school will find it useful to build up a small bank of questions which, when used with the pupils, reveal quickly and clearly their understanding of key concepts.

Principle 5
Diagnostic assessment

5.12   Teachers need to know what pupils find difficult, and why they find it difficult. Without the latter diagnosis any action to remove the difficulty will probably be ineffective. For example, failure to master a skill may be due to insufficient repetitive use, but more often the source of the problem is a conceptual misunderstanding which needs to be dealt with before any further practice is given. Failure in high-order skills (conceptual structures and general strategies) is often due to insufficient variety in the experiences provided. In general, *a statement that a pupil is not good at a particular aspect of mathematics should be qualified in terms of the various types of objectives:* the pupil might have forgotten a fact (such as a convention), been unable to perform a skill, been confused about a concept or had no general strategy for even starting the task required.

Principle 6
Opportunities within assessment procedures for pupils to show their capabilities

5.13   Test items are often considered to be good if their purposes are clearly defined, they are unambiguous and lead to a unique, correct response. For example, 'calculate 38 × 32' and 'solve the equation 2 (x − 1) = 10' might be considered to be two such items. They can be used to measure success or failure in a relatively narrow sense but they do not provide opportunities for pupils to show what they know and can do or to demonstrate higher order objectives. The following tasks offer much more scope:

'find different calculations or types of calculation which have an answer equal to 36'.
'find different equations which have one root, x = 10'.

These questions have many right answers and so such questions allow pupils to explore many different possibilities. Indeed, each question could be a complete half-hour test in itself and could well reveal more about the pupils' abilities than, say, 20 different questions of a closed nature. The ceiling is imposed by the pupils' abilities not by the teacher's perception of their abilities. *Assessment procedures should include a variety of approaches.*

Principle 7
Language demands

5.14   Language difficulties are often a barrier to pupils' mathematical progress. As a consequence teaching and learning resources are often chosen on the basis of the extent to which the authors have succeeded in reducing the amount and complexity of language demands. To follow this policy through into assessment is felt to be 'fair' if language demands in examinations are kept to a minimum. At 16-plus there is often criticism of some examinations on the grounds of excessive language demands. Moreover, there is strong evidence from the APU that pupils' performance is significantly affected by the language used in questions. But this is a vicious circle. If teaching and learning were to give more stress to 'mathematics as a means of communication' mathematics and language would be more closely linked together and the language component strengthened. Assessment and examinations based on such a

49

mathematics curriculum could then have a greater language component than is usually the case at present. A reduction in mathematical content has already been suggested as a means of enabling teachers to use a wider range of classroom approaches; it will also permit them to give greater emphasis to the development and use of language in mathematics.

Principle 8
Standardised testing

5.15   Standardised tests (norm referenced) are intended to provide information about the attainment of pupils in relation to other pupils of similar age. As such they are an indicator but it would be quite wrong if they were the only indicator used. They have serious limitations which may be highlighted by a simple application of some of the principles already considered. In practice they do not cover the full range of objectives as they pay relatively little attention to conceptual structures and almost none to general strategies. Nor do they reflect broad classroom approaches to the teaching and learning of mathematics as most require only written responses on short items. Moreover, they are not intended to provide diagnosis of pupils' strengths and weaknesses except in very general terms. One danger in attaching undue importance to such tests, especially at the point of transfer from one class or school to another, is that teacher expectations of the pupils can be considerably distorted by the results. *Standardised tests have their uses but need to be complemented by other methods of assessment.*

Principle 9
Criterion referenced testing

5.16   Criterion referenced tests are intended to provide information on the attainment of pupils in relation to particular criteria. For example, the criterion might be multiplication by a two-digit number, the measurement of length in millimetres using a ruler, or the solution of simple equations. There are two particular dangers. First of all, the criteria need to be expressed with precision as do the related test questions, in order to ensure that the tests measure what is intended. Unfortunately, it is easier to ask precise questions about facts and skills without reference to context. As a consequence a test result may show that a pupil can multiply by a two-digit number but would not reveal that the same pupil is able to apply this skill in a real situation. Secondly, there is a temptation to teach towards the criteria and when the test has been taken to start to repeat the cycle for the next set of criteria. Such an approach measures instant, often temporary, success rather than any lasting attainment. Although these dangers are present in other forms of tests and examinations they are especially present in criterion referenced tests (or associated types of assessment such as graded tests). Nevertheless, if criterion referenced tests can be devised to cover the full range of objectives and reflect broad classroom approaches, and if they are used sensibly, they will yield valuable information about pupils' attainment.

Principle 10
Assessment of personal qualities
5.17 The statement of aims given in Chapter 1 and their interpretation in the subsequent statements of objectives, criteria for content and classroom approaches are centrally concerned with the development of the personal qualities of the pupils. These need to be assessed but mainly in an informal way. In particular, consideration should be given to the following qualities:

(a) Work habits: imaginative, creative, flexible;
systematic;
independent in thought and action;
cooperative;
persistent.

(b) Attitudes: fascination with the subject;
interest and motivation;
pleasure and enjoyment from mathematical activities;
appreciation of the purpose, power and relevance of mathematics;
satisfaction derived from a sense of achievement;
confidence in an ability to do mathematics at an appropriate level.

If these personal qualities are missing there is something fundamentally wrong with the mathematics curriculum whatever the levels of achievement attained by the pupils.

51

6. Implementation

"Mathematics is a difficult subject both to teach and to learn."
(*Mathematics counts*, para. 228).

6.1 It is hoped that this paper will enable it to be a more rewarding experience for both teachers and pupils.

6.2 The headings within each chapter are intended to form a checklist as an instrument to be used both in planning and in evaluation. For example, when the staff of a school or a mathematics department are designing their mathematics curriculum they should consider carefully the aims listed in Chapter 1 and decide what are the main implications of each aim in terms of the objectives to be set for the pupils; the content to be covered; the classroom approaches to be followed; and the assessment procedures to be used. When the mathematics curriculum is implemented, the teachers should consider whether, in practice, there is evidence that the experiences of the pupils cover the aims overall with sufficient breadth, depth and balance. Consideration of this evidence might be done collectively by teachers at regular intervals, perhaps at the end of a term or the end of a year. Additionally an individual teacher might use the checklist of aims at more frequent intervals to monitor what is happening with a particular class or group of pupils in order that suitable action might be taken to redress any deficiencies or imbalances identified.

6.3 Similar action should be taken by schools on the use of separate checklists compiled from the chapters on objectives, criteria for content, classroom approaches and assessment procedures. The implications of each should be fully considered and implemented within the mathematics teaching.

6.4 Schools might find it useful to produce grid sheets for each of the separate checklists. These might be as in Figure 17: column 1 would contain, for example, the checklist of the aims of the mathematics curriculum; column 2 would be completed in the process of designing the mathematics curriculum; column 3 would contain the classroom evidence that the aims were being implemented. It may be better to have a separate sheet for each aspect: columns 1 and 2 could be a sheet within the school's agreed scheme of work; columns 1 and 3 could be a sheet to be used as necessary by the staff.

6.5 While this paper does not set out to be specific about

objectives and content at all stages from 5 to 16, Appendix 1 provides an illustrative example of the mathematical objectives considered to be achievable by most pupils at the ages of 11 and 16, though many pupils should do much more. Reference

Figure 17

The Mathematics Curriculum		
1. Aims	2. Design: implications	3. Implementation: evidence
Checklist		

should also be made to the set of objectives given in Appendix 1 of *Mathematics 5 – 11* and to the Foundation List proposed by the Cockcroft Committee (*Mathematics counts*, para. 458). It is important to ensure that the objectives are seen in relation to all that is said in the rest of the paper, that they reflect the aims and that they are acquired as a result of the broad classroom approaches proposed.

6.6 It is the responsibility of each school to develop a mathematics programme appropriate to its own pupils within a sound framework such as that offered by this paper.

APPENDIX 1

Mathematical objectives for most pupils at the ages of 11 and 16

This appendix deals specifically with those objectives which are content related. The other objectives are not dealt with here, but the reader should refer back to what is said about them in Chapter 2. For example, objective 20 (reasoning) does not lead to new content but is based on whatever content is otherwise required. It is essential that the objectives not amplified here should also be carefully considered because they are more general objectives and are most important.

The Cockcroft Report pointed out that there are certain mathematical tasks which an 'average' child can perform at age 11, which some 14 year olds cannot do and which some 7 year olds can do. This seven year difference clearly indicates that in planning their work teachers need to take into account the wide gap in understanding and skill which can exist between pupils of the same age. But at the same time they need to know what they can normally expect of most children of a given age. In making use of the list of objectives which are considered to be achievable targets for most pupils at the ages of 11 and 16, it needs to be recognised that there will be some children who will be behind on some of the items and others who will be ahead on all or most of the items listed. In the few cases where pupils have to struggle unduly to cover all of these objectives and experience frustration, failure and loss of confidence, the range of objectives is clearly too wide and needs to be reduced by schools accordingly. On the other hand many pupils will cover all of them relatively easily and so, for these pupils, schools will need to make considerable extensions.

The left-hand column contains the objectives for 11 year olds, with additions in the right-hand column for 16 year olds. Where there is no addition it should not be taken to mean that there are no differences between the two levels. In fact, the main differences are often in the greater depth of treatment; in the wider and more complex range of activities in which the content appears; and in the more extensive responses expected of the pupils.

To view this list of objectives as definitive in any sense would be contrary to the whole philosophy of this paper and detrimental to the mathematical needs of the pupils.

List of objectives

Objectives for most pupils at the age of 11

Objectives for most pupils at the age of 16

It is expected that many pupils will do much more.

A. FACTS

(Objectives 1 - 4) *Pupils need to remember:*

1. Terms

Qualitative mathematical language used in describing, identifying and classifying objects.
Pupils need to remember number names and to be able to record whole numbers from 0 to 9999 (verbal and digital form).
Number properties such as odd and even . . . . .

prime, square, triangular, factor, multiple.
Negative numbers.

Terms used in the number operations, such as addition, plus, more than.
The names of fractions ($\frac{1}{4}$, $\frac{1}{2}$, $\frac{3}{4}$, $\frac{1}{3}$, $\frac{2}{3}$, $\frac{1}{5}$, $\frac{1}{10}$) also numerator and denominator . . . . .

sum, difference, product, quotient.
sequences $\frac{1}{2}$, $\frac{1}{4}$, $\frac{1}{8}$, $\frac{1}{16}$, . . . and $\frac{1}{3}$, $\frac{1}{6}$, $\frac{1}{12}$, . . .

Terms used in decimals (up to two places of decimals).

Terms in percentages; ratio and proportion, rates of change.

Units of measurement in common use (Imperial and metric), including those of area, volume and capacity.

Age 11—*continued*
Current coins.

Names of common shapes in three and two dimensions. Terms such as side, diagonal, perimeter, area. Simple terms in probability and statistics including graphical representation.

Vocabulary to make sense of topic and reference books in mathematics at an appropriate level.

Age 16—*continued*

Wider range of shapes.

Wider range of graphical representation.

2. Notation

Number symbols 0 - 9. Place value.

Operation symbols: $+$, $-$, $\times$, $\div$.

Fractional notation. Decimal notation.

Equality and inequality signs ($=$, $>$, $<$).

Index notation; root sign $\sqrt{}$
Directed number notation.

Percentage sign. Ratio sign.

Angle notation (degrees).
π

3. Conventions

As used in 1 and 2.

Order of operations, for example in $a + b \times c$.

Use of brackets. Abbreviations in measurements: for example, metres (m), cubic metres (m^3), kilograms (kg).

Abbreviations such as mph.

Conventions on axes of graphs.

56

4. Results

Sums and products of pairs of numbers from 0 to 10 and their associated differences and quotients.

Equivalences of common fractions, decimals and percentages.

Common formulae (in words), for example for areas of rectangles and circles and the volume of cuboids.

Basic properties of common shapes.

Angle sum of a triangle. Pythagoras' Theorem.

B. SKILLS

(Objectives 5 - 9)

5. Performing basic operations

Four operations of number using whole numbers within their own level of understanding (multiplication and division by a single digit only).

Directed numbers in practical contexts.

Operations performed mentally or on paper as appropriate.

Four operations in realistic contexts of money and measurement (length, weight, time, temperature, area, volume and capacity).

Four operations of number involving up to two places of decimals, in the context of money and measurement.

Use fractions in everyday situations.

Formulae used in simple practical contexts.

Age 11—*continued* Age 16—*continued*

6. Sensible use of a calculator

Four operations of number with more complex data than in 5 (eg multiplication and division might be by larger numbers) . . . . .

Further complexities in data (ie raw data does not need to be simplified).

Check 'calculator' results.

Approximate to the results as a check on reasonableness.

7. Simple practical skills in mathematics

Use number and number operations in practical situations.
Carry out money transactions.
Measure with appropriate degrees of accuracy.

Read meters, clocks and dials of various kinds.

Tell the time using 12-hour and 24-hour clocks.
Make simple geometrical shapes in three and two dimensions.

8. Ability to communicate mathematics

Orally.
In writing.
Visually, using models, diagrams, charts, graphs.
Use of a wide range of printed material: workcards, textbooks, topic books, reference books, television, catalogues.

More precise use of language.
More extensive responses.
Wider range of visual representation.

Critical appraisal of information presented in the media, pamphlets and advertisements.
Forms used in adult life including employment.

9. The use of microcomputers in mathematical activities

(much developmental work still to be done)
To operate a machine using:
appropriate software;
simple programming
techniques.

C. CONCEPTUAL STRUCTURES
(Objectives 10 - 14)

10. Understanding basic concepts

A thorough understanding
of place value.
The nature of the four
operations.
Simple concepts of fractions
including equivalence.
Decimals in the context of
money and measurement.

Fuller understanding
of the decimal system.
Percentages.
Ratio and proportion.
Rates of change.

Understanding of money
Measurement as a means of
comparison using both
crude measures and
standard units (length,
weight, time, temperature,
area, volume and capacity).
Elementary notions of
probability and statistics.

Greater precision in
measurement.
Basic ideas of
randomness and
variability.
Various measures of
average.
Notion of spread.

Basic properties of common
three- and two-dimensional
shapes.
Broader aspects of number
such as tests of divisibility.

Wider range of shapes
and their properties.
Angles and bearings.

59

Age 11—*continued*   Age 16—*continued*

11. The relationships between concepts

Relationships between
number operations (eg
addition and
multiplication).

Relationships between
fractions, decimals and
percentages.

Relationships between
distance, time and
speed.

Relationship between a
fraction and a ratio.

Relationships between the
values of coins.
Relationships between other
units of measurement.
Relationships between
results (where a result can
be obtained from a known
result: eg 5 + 6 is one more
than 5 + 5 or 84 × 8 is 84
more than 84 × 7).

12. Selecting appropriate data

13. Using mathematics in context

14. Interpreting results

D. GENERAL STRATEGIES
(Objectives 15 - 22)

15. Ability to estimate

16. Ability to approximate

17. Trial and error methods

18. Simplifying difficult tasks

19. Looking for pattern

20. Reasoning

21. Making and testing hypotheses

22. Proving and disproving

E. PERSONAL QUALITIES
(Objectives 23, 24)

23. Good work habits:
imaginative, creative, flexible;
systematic;
independent in thought and action;
cooperative;
persistent.

24. Positive attitudes to mathematics
fascination with the subject;
interest and motivation;
pleasure and enjoyment from mathematical activities;
appreciation of the purpose, power and relevance of
mathematics;
satisfaction derived from a sense of achievement;
confidence in an ability to do mathematics at an appropriate
level.

APPENDIX 2

Differentiation: An illustrative example

The function of this appendix is to look in more detail at the illustrative example referred to in Chapter 3, para. 3.6, where curricular differentiation was being discussed.

Consideration of the volumes of open boxes which can be made from a 24cm square sheet is an activity suitable for pupils who know how to find the volume of a cuboid and can use a calculator where necessary.

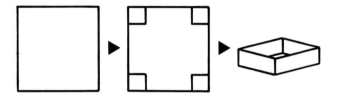

The dimensions of this box are 22cm, 22cm and 1cm.
The volume = 22 x 22 x 1 = 484 cm³
What other boxes can be produced? What are their volumes?
What is the largest volume which can be produced?

Table 1

Length of the side of the corner square (cm)	Dimensions of the open box (cm)			Volume of the open box (cm³)
1	22	22	1	484
2	20	20	2	800
3	18	18	3	972
4	16	16	4	1024
5	14	14	5	980
6	12	12	6	864
7	10	10	7	700
8	8	8	8	512
9	6	6	9	324

Is 1024 cm³ the largest volume? It would be appropriate for many pupils to test with corner squares of 3.9 cm and 4.1 cm, that is, on either side of 4 cm to see what happens.

The resulting volumes are, respectively, as follows:

$16.2 \times 16.2 \times 3.9 = 1023.516 \text{ cm}^3$
$15.8 \times 15.8 \times 4.1 = 1023.524 \text{ cm}^3$

As each of these is equal to 1024 cm³, correct to the nearest whole number, it seems reasonable to assume that this is, in fact, the maximum volume.

It might now be appropriate for some pupils to extend the investigation and to consider open boxes made from sheets which are not square, for example, a rectangular sheet 24 cm by 18 cm.

Table 2

Length of the side of the corner square (cm)	Dimensions of the open box (cm)		Volume of the open box (cm³)
1	22	16	1	352
2	20	14	2	560
3	18	12	3	648
4	16	10	4	640
5	14	8	5	560
6	12	6	6	432
7	10	4	7	280
8	8	2	8	112

Is 648 cm³ the largest volume? Repeating the former procedure, corner squares of sides 2.9 cm and 3.1 cm might be used. The respective volumes would be:

$18.2 \times 12.2 \times 2.9 = 643.916 \text{ cm}^3$
$17.8 \times 11.8 \times 3.1 = 651.124 \text{ cm}^3$

This time, the initial hypothesis has been proved to be wrong. It would be appropriate now to follow this up with further calculations with corner squares between 3 cm and 4 cm to find a more accurate value for the maximum volume.

In these activities, pupils might be encouraged to represent the results graphically. For example, the graph of volume plotted against the length of the side of the corner squares cut from a 24cm square sheet would be as shown:

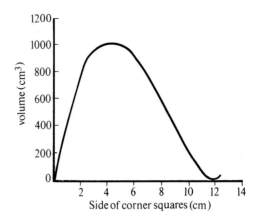

This might be used to provide further information, for example, to give the possible approximate dimensions of a box whose volume is 1000 cm³ a calculator might then be used to find the dimensions more accurately.

When working with more able pupils the volume might also be expressed algebraically. For example, if s cm represents the side of a square sheet, c cm represents the side of the corner squares and V cm³ represents the volume of the open box, then

$$V = c(s - 2c)^2$$

This formula might then be used, possibly with a graph plotter on a micro-computer, to draw graphs illustrating the variations in the volumes of the boxes made from different sizes of square sheets. The set of graphs might enable the pupil to form a hypothesis about the size of the corner square to be cut away from a square sheet of any given size in order to produce the box of maximum volume. The hypothesis would be confirmed or rejected only when calculus or advanced algebraic methods are used at a later stage.

APPENDIX 3

References

This is a list of publications referred to in the text and is not intended to be a bibliography of recommended books.

Mathematics counts: Report of the Committee of Inquiry into the teaching of mathematics in schools under the chairmanship of Dr W H Cockcroft. HMSO, 1982. £6.25.

Children's understanding of mathematics: 11-16: by Kathleen M Hart. A report from the Concepts in Secondary Mathematics and Science (CSMS) Project based at Chelsea College. John Murray, 1981. £8.95.

Curriculum 11-16: Towards a statement of entitlement. HMSO, 1983. £3.50.

Mathematics 5-11: No.9 in the HMI 'Matters for discussion' series. HMSO, 1979. £4.75.

Mathematical development: Reports of surveys of the mathematical achievements of pupils aged 11 and 15 conducted by the Assessment of Performance Unit. HMSO, 1980-82. £5.00-£6.75.

Microcomputers and mathematics in schools: A discussion paper by T J Fletcher HMI. DES, 1983. (Free.)

Curriculum Matters: an HMI series

Two titles already published are:

1: English from 5 to 16: HMSO, 1984. £1.50.
ISBN 0 11 270472 7.

2: The curriculum from 5 to 16: HMSO, 1985. £2.00.
ISBN 0 11 270568 5.

In the mathematics area, the following publications relating to the Cockcroft report are available free of charge from Publications Despatch Centre, DES, Honeypot Lane, Stanmore, Middlesex:

Blueprint for numeracy: An employer's guide to the Cockcroft report. DES, 1983. A 40-page booklet which highlights the principal findings of the Committee and draws employers' attention to the action they are recommended to take.

Cockcroft: An introduction for primary schools. DES, 1983. Only a 4-page leaflet, but it contains a great deal of useful information.

Printed in the UK for HMSO   Dd 8856301   C50   4/85